CONSIDERED TO BE THE NEXT STEP IN HUMAN EVOLUTION, MUTANTS DISCOVER THEIR HERITAGE AT P...
...UPERHUMAN POWERS AND ABILITIES. BUT RATHER THAN BEING CELEBRATED FOR THEIR GIFTS, MUTA...
A WORLD THAT'S NEVER HATED OR FEARED THEM MORE. WITH THE FATE OF THEIR RACE HANGING IN T...
HEROES WHO WILL COURAGEOUSLY LEAD THEM INTO THE FUTURE. MUTANTKIND NEEDS...

EXTRAORDINARY X MEN

X-HAVEN

JEFF LEMIRE
WRITER

HUMBERTO RAMOS
PENCILER

VICTOR OLAZABA
INKER

EDGAR DELGADO
COLORIST

VC'S JOE CARAMAGNA
LETTERER

COVER ART BY **HUMBERTO RAMOS & EDGAR DELGADO**

CHRISTINA HARRINGTON
ASSISTANT EDITOR

DANIEL KETCHUM
EDITOR

MARK PANICCIA
X-MEN GROUP EDITOR

X-MEN CREATED BY STAN LEE & JACK KIRBY

COLLECTION EDITOR: JENNIFER GRÜNWALD
ASSOCIATE EDITOR: SARAH BRUNSTAD
ASSOCIATE MANAGING EDITOR: ALEX STARBUCK
EDITOR, SPECIAL PROJECTS: MARK D. BEAZLEY
VP, PRODUCTION & SPECIAL PROJECTS: JEFF YOUNGQUIST
SVP PRINT, SALES & MARKETING: DAVID GABRIEL
BOOK DESIGNER: JAY BOWEN

EDITOR IN CHIEF: AXEL ALONSO
CHIEF CREATIVE OFFICER: JOE QUESADA
PUBLISHER: DAN BUCKLEY
EXECUTIVE PRODUCER: ALAN FINE

...TRAORDINARY X-MEN VOL. 1: X-HAVEN. Contains material originally published in magazine form as EXTRAORDINARY X-MEN #1-5. First printing 2016. ISBN# 978-0-7851-9934-2. Published by MARVEL WORLDWIDE, ..., a subsidiary of MARVEL ENTERTAINMENT, LLC. OFFICE OF PUBLICATION: 135 West 50th Street, New York, NY 10020. Copyright © 2016 MARVEL No similarity between any of the names, characters, persons, ...d/or institutions in this magazine with those of any living or dead person or institution is intended, and any such similarity which may exist is purely coincidental. **Printed in Canada.** ALAN FINE, President, Marvel ...ertainment; DAN BUCKLEY, President, TV, Publishing & Brand Management; JOE QUESADA, Chief Creative Officer; TOM BREVOORT, SVP of Publishing; DAVID BOGART, SVP of Business Affairs & Operations, Publishing & ...rtnership; C.B. CEBULSKI, VP of Brand Management & Development, Asia; DAVID GABRIEL, SVP of Sales & Marketing, Publishing; JEFF YOUNGQUIST, VP of Production & Special Projects; DAN CARR, Executive Director ... Publishing Technology; ALEX MORALES, Director of Publishing Operations; SUSAN CRESPI, Production Manager; STAN LEE, Chairman Emeritus. For information regarding advertising in Marvel Comics or on Marvel. ...m, please contact Vit DeBellis, Integrated Sales Manager, at vdebellis@marvel.com. For Marvel subscription inquiries, please call 888-511-5480. **Manufactured between 3/4/2016 and 4/11/2016 by SOLISCO** ...NTERS, SCOTT, QC, CANADA.

987654321

HOW DID IT COME TO THIS?

"WE'VE LOST *SO MUCH* ALREADY. THE X-MEN, MUTANTKIND'S PLACE IN THE WORLD...*SCOTT*.

"I WAS FOOLISH. I THOUGHT IT COULDN'T GET *ANY WORSE*. BUT I WAS WRONG. I WAS *SO WRONG*."

I'VE TRIED TO KEEP IT GOING. I'VE--I'VE DONE THINGS I NEVER THOUGHT I WOULD, JUST TO KEEP THE DREAM ALIVE. TO KEEP *THIS PLACE* ALIVE. BUT NOW--

"NOW *SOMETHING ELSE* HAS HAPPENED. SOMETHING THAT *CHANGES EVERYTHING*... ALL MY PLANS.

"I *CANNOT* AFFORD TO WAIT ANY LONGER AND I AM *SCARED* FOR WHAT COMES NEXT."

I--I DON'T KNOW HOW YOU DID THIS ALL THOSE YEARS...

SH-NCK!

<P-PLEASE, DON'T HURT OUR DAUGHTER!>

<I AM NOT HERE TO HURT HER, OR YOU... I A HERE TO TAKE YO SOMEWHERE SAFE.>

<MY NAME IS ILLYANA. WHAT IS YOURS?>

<SAPNA.>

<YOU DO NOT NEED TO BE AFRAID ANYMORE, SAPNA. I WILL HELP YOU. DO YOU TRUST ME? WILL YOU COME WITH ME?>

<Y-YES.>

THE STUDENTS ARE STARTING TO WEAR DOWN, ORORO. THEY'RE DOING THEIR BEST TO KEEP UP WITH THE NEW ARRIVALS BUT--

I KNOW. BUT, LIKE US, THEY DON'T HAVE A CHOICE. WE JUST HAVE TO *FIND A WAY.*

THEY'RE JUST KIDS, ORORO.

AND *THEY ARE MUTANTS.*

NOW MORE THAN EVER, EVERY MUTANT COUNTS.

KRZZZT-- KZZZZT!

HAVE YOU TOLD THEM THE *NEWS* YET?

NOT YET. THEY HAVE ENOUGH TO DEAL WITH. HERE SHE COMES--

MAGIK-- ILLYANA, YOU'RE HURT!

I'M FINE. JUST A FLESH WOUND. BUT THE GIRL IS VERY ILL. SHE NEEDS MEDICAL ATTENTION...THE TERRIGEN MIST HIT HER HARD.

--AND THIS IS WHY WE HAVE TO TOTALLY RETHINK THE OLD PARADIGMS OF ANTHROPOLOGICAL THOUGHT. THINGS ARE NOW SHIFTING SO FAST THAT WE CAN'T AFFORD TO BE STATIC IN OUR THINKING.

EMPIRE STATE UNIVERSITY. MANHATTAN.

AND THAT'S IT FOR TODAY. MIDTERM PAPERS ARE DUE NEXT FRIDAY, PEOPLE.

HEY, JEAN, YOU COMING OUT TONIGHT?

NOT SURE, I HAVE A BUNCH OF WORK TO CATCH UP ON.

AW, COME ON, JEAN! YOU'RE ONLY YOUNG ONCE.

THAT'S WHAT *YOU* THINK.

WHAT'S THAT SUPPOSED TO MEAN?

NOTHING. I'LL SEE YOU TONIGHT.

WHAT...?

LAKE BAIKAL, RUSSIA.

FORMERLY THE UST-ORDYNSKI COLLECTIVE FARM.

GRRRR

KRRZT!

ARE YOU SURE NIGHTCRAWLER IS HERE, ILLYANA?

CEREBRA LOCATED HIM HERE THIS MORNING BEFORE I LEFT X-HAVEN.

PIOTR, IS THAT...?

DO YOU THINK KURT COULD POSSIBLY FIND SOMEPLACE WITH A *NARROWER* STAIRCASE?

MAYBE HE DIDN'T WANT YOU TO VISIT. OR MAYBE YOU'VE GOTTEN *BIGGER*.

HUMPH! COULDN'T YOU JUST TELEPORT US THERE, ILLYANA?

WHAT WOULD BE THE FUN IN THAT? BESIDES, I WANT TO SEE THE LOOK ON HIS FACE WHEN HE OPENS THE DOOR AND SEES US.

THOOM!

STAY BEHIND ME.

OH, PLEASE.

KURT?!

HE'S GONE...

...AT LEAST *MOST OF* HIM IS.

MANITOBA, CANADA.

LOGAN.

JEANNIE. FIGURED YOU'D CATCH UP TO ME SOONER OR LATER. YOU ALWAYS DO.

YOU START TALKING TO YOURSELF, MEANS IT'S TIME TO GO, OLD MAN.

YEAH, YEAH. I'M ABOUT SICK OF THIS JOINT ANYHOW, BUB.

I CAN SEE YOUR MEMORIES, LOGAN. I KNOW WHAT YOU WENT THROUGH...

I KNOW WHAT HAPPENED.

YOU SHOULD STAY AWAY THEN, JEANNIE. BAD ENOUGH I GOTTA SEE WHAT'S IN THERE.

IT WASN'T YOUR FAULT, LOGAN.

REALLY, RED?

I TRIED TO LIVE A "NORMAL" LIFE, WHATEVER I THOUGHT THAT WAS. AND LOOK AT YOU. LOOK AT HOW YOU'VE BEEN LIVING.

YOU WANT TO TALK ABOUT DESTINY? WELL, YOU AND I ARE DESTINED TO BE X-MEN.

I'LL KEEP AN EYE ON YOU. I'LL LET YOU KNOW THE SECOND I SENSE YOU LOSING CONTROL. I'LL NEVER LET IT GET THAT FAR. I PROMISE.

YOU CAN TRUST ME, LOGAN.

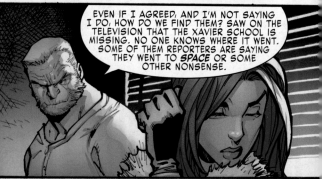

EVEN IF I AGREED, AND I'M NOT SAYING I DO, HOW DO WE FIND THEM? SAW ON THE TELEVISION THAT THE XAVIER SCHOOL IS MISSING. NO ONE KNOWS WHERE IT WENT. SOME OF THEM REPORTERS ARE SAYING THEY WENT TO SPACE OR SOME OTHER NONSENSE.

WE CAN CALL THEM. AND THEY AREN'T IN SPACE.

SO YOU'RE IN? YOU'RE COMING WITH ME? COME ON, LOGAN... COME ON!

I NEVER COULD SAY NO TO YOU, JEANNIE.

...BUT I AIN'T WEARING NO DAMN COSTUME.

FORGE! MOST OF THE REFUGEES ARE INSIDE THE SCHOOL, BUT WE CAN'T KEEP THE DEMONS OUT FOR LONG! WE NEED THAT SHIELD!

GRRRAAAAARR!

UNGH!

YOU MUST GET UP, ORORO.

GRAAARRR!

GET UP.

--WHA--?

PROFESSOR?

GET UP AND FIGHT.

#1 VARIANT BY J. SCOTT CAMPBELL & NEI RUFFINO

ILLYANA?

ILLYANA?!

DO YOU SEE, YOUNG PIOTR? DO YOU SEE THAT THIS IS THE END?

<NO! WHERE IS MY SISTER?! WHAT HAVE YOU DONE WITH ILLYANA?!>

IT WASN'T ME...IT WAS THE *INHUMANS.* AND CYCLOPS--SCOTT-- THEY *DOOMED US ALL.*

<KURT, I-I DON'T UNDERSTAND.>

THEY WILL PAY THE PENALTY OF ETERNAL DESTRUCTION...

AWAY FROM THE PRESENCE OF THE LORD AND FROM THE GLORY OF HIS POWER.

MANHATTAN.

SHRACK!

M-MUTANTS! DON'T HURT US!

THEY'RE JUST CHILDREN! PLEASE--STAY AWAY!

SO IT'S LIKE THAT AGAIN, HUH?

IT'S LIKE THAT.

YOU OKAY, JEANNIE?

I'M FINE. YOU?

I'LL LIVE.

OH, LOOK, YOU TWO HAVE A CUTE FATHER-DAUGHTER THING GOING NOW, HUH? OR I GUESS MORE LIKE GRANDFATHER-DAUGHTER, RIGHT?

WAIT...IT IS A GRANDFATHER-DAUGHTER THING, RIGHT? BECAUSE IF IT'S NOT, THAT IS JUST CREEPY.

DO YOU HAVE THEIR SCENT, LOGAN?

THIS WAY. BUT THERE'S SOMETHING ELSE, TOO...

#2 VARIANT BY KEVIN WADA

WE ARE NOT THE ENEMY. NOW, MORE THAN EVER, WE MUST *ALL STAND TOGETHER.*

...WE *WILL NOT* GIVE UP ON YOU.

EVEN THOUGH YOU MAY *FEAR US.* EVEN THOUGH YOU MAY *HATE US...*

HELL OF A SPEECH, ORORO. BUT NOW WHAT?

NOW?

TO ME, MY X-MEN.

NICE.

ILLYANA, TAKE US HOME.

SHRAK

NEXT:
WEIRDWORLD

#3 VARIANT BY CLAY MANN & JUSTIN PONSOR

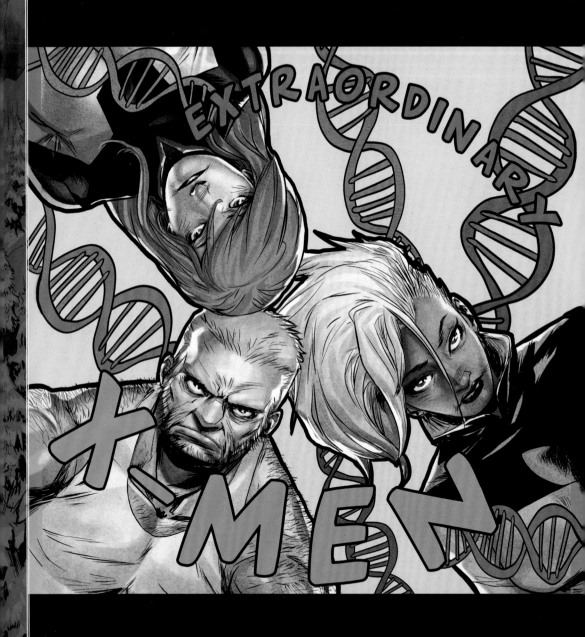